D1310880

Personal Trainer Client Log Book

This Log Book Belongs to :

....

Client Profile

Name

Address

Phone

Email

Weight

Height

Chest

Waist

BMI

Appointments

-
-
-
-
-
-

Price :   **$**

Goals

- [ ]
- [ ]
- [ ]

Notes

Exercise	Sets	Reps	Tempo	Rest	Coaching Tips

Client Profile

Name

Address

Phone

Email

Weight

Height

Chest

Waist

BMI

Appointments

-
-
-
-
-
-

Price :   **$**

Goals

☐

☐

☐

Notes

Exercise	Sets	Reps	Tempo	Rest	Coaching Tips

Client Profile

Name

Address

Phone

Email

Weight

Height

Chest

Waist

BMI

Appointments

-
-
-
-
-
-

Price :   **$**

Goals

- [ ]
- [ ]
- [ ]

Notes

Exercise	Sets	Reps	Tempo	Rest	Coaching Tips

Client Profile

Name

Address

Phone

Email

Weight

Height

Chest

Waist

BMI

Appointments

-
-
-
-
-
-

Price :   **$**

Goals

☐

☐

☐

Notes

Exercise	Sets	Reps	Tempo	Rest	Coaching Tips

Client Profile

Name

Address

Phone

Email

Weight

Height

Chest

Waist

BMI

Appointments

-
-
-
-
-
-

Price : **$**

Goals

☐

☐

☐

Notes

Exercise	Sets	Reps	Tempo	Rest	Coaching Tips

Client Profile

Name

Address

Phone

Email

Weight

Height

Chest

Waist

BMI

Appointments

-
-
-
-
-
-

Price :   **$**

Goals

☐

☐

☐

Notes

Exercise	Sets	Reps	Tempo	Rest	Coaching Tips

Client Profile

Name

Address

Phone

Email

Weight

Height

Chest

Waist

BMI

Appointments

-
-
-
-
-
-

Price :   **$**

Goals

☐

☐

☐

Notes

Exercise	Sets	Reps	Tempo	Rest	Coaching Tips

Client Profile

Name

Address

Phone

Email

Weight

Height

Chest

Waist

BMI

Appointments

-
-
-
-
-
-

Price : **$**

Goals

☐

☐

☐

Notes

Exercise	Sets	Reps	Tempo	Rest	Coaching Tips

Client Profile

Name

Address

Phone

Email

Weight

Height

Chest

Waist

BMI

Appointments

-
-
-
-
-
-

Price : **$**

Goals

- [ ]
- [ ]
- [ ]

Notes

Exercise	Sets	Reps	Tempo	Rest	Coaching Tips

Client Profile

Name

Address

Phone

Email

Weight

Height

Chest

Waist

BMI

Appointments

-
-
-
-
-
-

Price : $

Goals

☐

☐

☐

Notes

Exercise	Sets	Reps	Tempo	Rest	Coaching Tips

Client Profile

Name

Address

Phone

Email

Weight

Height

Chest

Waist

BMI

Appointments

-
-
-
-
-
-

Price :   **$**

Goals

☐

☐

☐

Notes

Exercise	Sets	Reps	Tempo	Rest	Coaching Tips

Client Profile

Name

Address

Phone

Email

Weight

Height

Chest

Waist

BMI

Appointments

-
-
-
-
-
-

Price :   **$**

Goals

☐

☐

☐

Notes

Exercise	Sets	Reps	Tempo	Rest	Coaching Tips

Client Profile

Name

Address

Phone

Email

Weight

Height

Chest

Waist

BMI

Appointments

-
-
-
-
-
-

Price :   **$**

Goals

☐

☐

☐

Notes

Exercise	Sets	Reps	Tempo	Rest	Coaching Tips

Client Profile

Name

Address

Phone

Email

Weight

Height

Chest

Waist

BMI

Appointments

-
-
-
-
-
-

Price :   **$**

Goals

- [ ]
- [ ]
- [ ]

Notes

Exercise	Sets	Reps	Tempo	Rest	Coaching Tips

Client Profile

Name

Address

Phone

Email

Weight

Height

Chest

Waist

BMI

Appointments

-
-
-
-
-
-

Price : **$**

Goals

☐

☐

☐

Notes

Exercise	Sets	Reps	Tempo	Rest	Coaching Tips

Client Profile

Name

Address

Phone

Email

Weight

Height

Chest

Waist

BMI

Appointments

-
-
-
-
-
-

Price : **$**

Goals

☐

☐

☐

Notes

Exercise	Sets	Reps	Tempo	Rest	Coaching Tips

Client Profile

Name

Address

Phone

Email

Weight

Height

Chest

Waist

BMI

Appointments

-
-
-
-
-
-

Price : $

Goals

- [ ]
- [ ]
- [ ]

Notes

Exercise	Sets	Reps	Tempo	Rest	Coaching Tips

Client Profile

Name

Address

Phone

Email

Weight

Height

Chest

Waist

BMI

Appointments

-
-
-
-
-
-

Price :   **$**

Goals

- [ ]
- [ ]
- [ ]

Notes

Exercise	Sets	Reps	Tempo	Rest	Coaching Tips

Client Profile

Name

Address

Phone

Email

Weight

Height

Chest

Waist

BMI

Appointments

-
-
-
-
-
-

Price :   **$**

Goals

☐

☐

☐

Notes

Exercise	Sets	Reps	Tempo	Rest	Coaching Tips

Client Profile

Name

Address

Phone

Email

Weight

Height

Chest

Waist

BMI

Appointments

-
-
-
-
-
-

Price :   **$**

Goals

☐

☐

☐

Notes

Exercise	Sets	Reps	Tempo	Rest	Coaching Tips

Client Profile

Name

Address

Phone

Email

Weight

Height

Chest

Waist

BMI

Appointments

-
-
-
-
-
-

Price : $

Goals

- [ ]
- [ ]
- [ ]

Notes

Exercise	Sets	Reps	Tempo	Rest	Coaching Tips

Client Profile

Name

Address

Phone

Email

Weight

Height

Chest

Waist

BMI

Appointments

-
-
-
-
-
-

Price : **$**

Goals

- [ ]
- [ ]
- [ ]

Notes

Exercise	Sets	Reps	Tempo	Rest	Coaching Tips

Client Profile

Name

Address

Phone

Email

Weight

Height

Chest

Waist

BMI

Appointments

-
-
-
-
-
-

Price : **$**

Goals

☐

☐

☐

Notes

Exercise	Sets	Reps	Tempo	Rest	Coaching Tips

Client Profile

Name

Address

Phone

Email

Weight

Height

Chest

Waist

BMI

Appointments

-
-
-
-
-
-

Price : $

Goals

☐

☐

☐

Notes

Exercise	Sets	Reps	Tempo	Rest	Coaching Tips

Client Profile

Name

Address

Phone

Email

Weight

Height

Chest

Waist

BMI

Appointments

-
-
-
-
-
-

Price : $

Goals

☐

☐

☐

Notes

Exercise	Sets	Reps	Tempo	Rest	Coaching Tips

Client Profile

Name

Address

Phone

Email

Weight

Height

Chest

Waist

BMI

Appointments

-
-
-
-
-
-

Price : **$**

Goals

☐

☐

☐

Notes

Exercise	Sets	Reps	Tempo	Rest	Coaching Tips

Client Profile

Name

Address

Phone

Email

Weight

Height

Chest

Waist

BMI

Appointments

-
-
-
-
-
-

Price :   **$**

Goals

- [ ]
- [ ]
- [ ]

Notes

Exercise	Sets	Reps	Tempo	Rest	Coaching Tips

Client Profile

Name

Address

Phone

Email

Weight

Height

Chest

Waist

BMI

Appointments

-
-
-
-
-
-

Price :   **$**

Goals

☐

☐

☐

Notes

Exercise	Sets	Reps	Tempo	Rest	Coaching Tips

Client Profile

Name

Address

Phone

Email

Weight

Height

Chest

Waist

BMI

Appointments

-
-
-
-
-
-

Price :   **$**

Goals

☐

☐

☐

Notes

Exercise	Sets	Reps	Tempo	Rest	Coaching Tips

Client Profile

Name

Address

Phone

Email

Weight

Height

Chest

Waist

BMI

Appointments

-
-
-
-
-
-

Price : **$**

Goals

☐

☐

☐

Notes

Exercise	Sets	Reps	Tempo	Rest	Coaching Tips

Client Profile

Name

Address

Phone

Email

Weight

Height

Chest

Waist

BMI

Appointments

-
-
-
-
-
-

Price :   **$**

Goals

☐

☐

☐

Notes

Exercise	Sets	Reps	Tempo	Rest	Coaching Tips

Client Profile

Name

Address

Phone

Email

Weight

Height

Chest

Waist

BMI

Appointments

-
-
-
-
-
-

Price :   **$**

Goals

☐

☐

☐

Notes

Exercise	Sets	Reps	Tempo	Rest	Coaching Tips

Client Profile

Name

Address

Phone

Email

Weight

Height

Chest

Waist

BMI

Appointments

-
-
-
-
-
-

Price : **$**

Goals

☐

☐

☐

Notes

Exercise	Sets	Reps	Tempo	Rest	Coaching Tips

Client Profile

Name

Address

Phone

Email

Weight

Height

Chest

Waist

BMI

Appointments

-
-
-
-
-
-

Price : **$**

Goals

- [ ]
- [ ]
- [ ]

Notes

Exercise	Sets	Reps	Tempo	Rest	Coaching Tips

Client Profile

Name

Address

Phone

Email

Weight

Height

Chest

Waist

BMI

Appointments

-
-
-
-
-
-

Price :   **$**

Goals

☐

☐

☐

Notes

Exercise	Sets	Reps	Tempo	Rest	Coaching Tips

Client Profile

Name

Address

Phone

Email

Weight

Height

Chest

Waist

BMI

Appointments

-
-
-
-
-
-

Price :   **$**

Goals

☐

☐

☐

Notes

Exercise	Sets	Reps	Tempo	Rest	Coaching Tips

Client Profile

Name

Address

Phone

Email

Weight

Height

Chest

Waist

BMI

Appointments

-
-
-
-
-
-

Price :   **$**

Goals

☐

☐

☐

Notes

Exercise	Sets	Reps	Tempo	Rest	Coaching Tips

Client Profile

Name

Address

Phone

Email

Weight

Height

Chest

Waist

BMI

Appointments

-
-
-
-
-
-

Price : **$**

Goals

☐

☐

☐

Notes

Exercise	Sets	Reps	Tempo	Rest	Coaching Tips

Client Profile

Name

Address

Phone

Email

Weight

Height

Chest

Waist

BMI

Appointments

-
-
-
-
-
-

Price :   **$**

Goals

☐

☐

☐

Notes

Exercise	Sets	Reps	Tempo	Rest	Coaching Tips

Client Profile

Name

Address

Phone

Email

Weight

Height

Chest

Waist

BMI

Appointments

-
-
-
-
-
-

Price :   **$**

Goals

☐

☐

☐

Notes

Exercise	Sets	Reps	Tempo	Rest	Coaching Tips

Client Profile

Name

Address

Phone

Email

Weight

Height

Chest

Waist

BMI

Appointments

-
-
-
-
-
-

Price : **$**

Goals

- [ ]
- [ ]
- [ ]

Notes

Exercise	Sets	Reps	Tempo	Rest	Coaching Tips

Client Profile

Name

Address

Phone

Email

Weight

Height

Chest

Waist

BMI

Appointments

-
-
-
-
-
-

Price : **$**

Goals

☐

☐

☐

Notes

Exercise	Sets	Reps	Tempo	Rest	Coaching Tips

Client Profile

Name

Address

Phone

Email

Weight

Height

Chest

Waist

BMI

Appointments

-
-
-
-
-
-

Price :   **$**

Goals

☐

☐

☐

Notes

Exercise	Sets	Reps	Tempo	Rest	Coaching Tips

Client Profile

Name

Address

Phone

Email

Weight

Height

Chest

Waist

BMI

Appointments

-
-
-
-
-
-

Price : **$**

Goals

☐

☐

☐

Notes

Exercise	Sets	Reps	Tempo	Rest	Coaching Tips

Client Profile

Name

Address

Phone

Email

Weight

Height

Chest

Waist

BMI

Appointments

-
-
-
-
-
-

Price :   **$**

Goals

☐

☐

☐

Notes

Exercise	Sets	Reps	Tempo	Rest	Coaching Tips

Client Profile

Name

Address

Phone

Email

Weight

Height

Chest

Waist

BMI

Appointments

-
-
-
-
-
-

Price : **$**

Goals

- [ ]
- [ ]
- [ ]

Notes

Exercise	Sets	Reps	Tempo	Rest	Coaching Tips

Client Profile

Name

Address

Phone

Email

Weight

Height

Chest

Waist

BMI

Appointments

-
-
-
-
-
-

Price :   **$**

Goals

☐

☐

☐

Notes

Exercise	Sets	Reps	Tempo	Rest	Coaching Tips

Client Profile

Name

Address

Phone

Email

Weight

Height

Chest

Waist

BMI

Appointments

-
-
-
-
-
-

Price :   **$**

Goals

- [ ]
- [ ]
- [ ]

Notes

Exercise	Sets	Reps	Tempo	Rest	Coaching Tips

Client Profile

Name

Address

Phone

Email

Weight

Height

Chest

Waist

BMI

Appointments

-
-
-
-
-
-

Price :   **$**

Goals

☐

☐

☐

Notes

Exercise	Sets	Reps	Tempo	Rest	Coaching Tips

Made in United States
Orlando, FL
18 May 2022

17987189R00057